MW00620585

# AWESOME JATAKA TALES

SHREE BOOKS

**Awesome Jataka Tales**
ISBN: 978-93-5049-419-6

First Edition: 2013

© Shree Book Centre

Printed in India

*Retold by*
Sunita Pant Bansal

*All rights reserved. No part of this publication may be reproduced or transmitted in any form or by any means, electronic or mechanical, including photocopying, recording, or by any information storage and retrieval system, without permission in writing from the publishers.*

*Published by*

**SHREE BOOK CENTRE**
8, Kakad Industrial Estate, S. Keer Marg
Off L.J. Road, Matunga (W)
Mumbai - 400016 (India)
Tel : 91-22-24377516 / 24374559
Telefax: 91-22-24309183
E-mail: sales@shreebookcentre.com

# CONTENTS

# PREFACE

The Jataka Tales, written more than two thousand years ago, consist of more than five hundred stories about the previous lives of the Buddha in both human and animal forms. These stories, told by the Buddha himself, were aimed at teaching his disciples the importance of moral values in life.

In these stories, one comes across a delicate bond of friendship brewing up between an elephant and a dog; a man deciding to stand by his best friend; a merchant sticking to the virtue of honesty and a monkey using his wit to overcome trouble. They teach the children in simple ways the goodness of qualities like trust, self-sacrifice, friendship, bonding, sharing, and presence of mind.

This book, a carefully picked bouquet of six moral-based stories, has colourful illustrations. The simple language makes reading easier for children, and the dialogue blurbs allow the characters to speak their mind. The meanings of difficult words at the end of the book help children to build their vocabulary.

# Finding A New Spring

In a small village, there lived a Merchant who sold various kinds of goods. One day, he decided to sell his goods in a faraway town for higher profits. He hired some men to accompany him on the journey across a desert. After loading several carts with

goods, water, rice and firewood, they set off for the town.

When the Merchant and his men reached the desert, the sun was shining, making it unbearable to walk on the hot sand. So, they decided to continue their journey during night when the sand would cool down. One of the men knew how to find the way by charting the stars. So, he guided them through the desert. They travelled all night without stopping. They halted and camped at daybreak. They unyoked the oxen and fed them.

They lit a fire and cooked food. Each one had his fill. To protect the oxen from the sun, a huge cover was spread over the carts. Then,

See! They were really hungry.

the men rested till sunset. In the evening,
before they moved, they watered and fed
the oxen, and cooked and ate food.

One morning, the group's guide
announced, "One more night, and then we
will reach the town." Everyone was happy
to hear this, since they all were tired. It
being their last night in the desert, the

Merchant suggested, "We can throw away the extra water and the firewood, because tomorrow we will reach our destination. Now let us move!"

The guide took his position at the head of the line of carts. However, instead of guiding others, he lay down in the cart and fell asleep.

The oxen walked all night. The guide woke up at daybreak and looked at the last stars fading into the light. He exclaimed, "Stop! We are in the same place as we began. The oxen must have turned around while I slept!"

They released the oxen, but there was no water to drink or firewood to cook. Tired

and thirsty, the men complained, "Without firewood and water, what will we do? We are lost!"

The Merchant thought, 'This is not the time for me to rest. I must find water. The men and the oxen cannot move, and no food can be cooked. If I give up, we all will die. There must be water somewhere here.'

I have to find water at any cost.

He walked around and studied the ground carefully. Finally, he saw some grass and exclaimed, "There must be water below the ground here! Otherwise this grass would not grow."

He ran back crying, "Get the spade and the hammer, and come with me."

The men ran to the spot where the merchant

saw the grass. They started digging and after a while they struck a rock. They could not dig any further.

The merchant jumped into the hole that they had dug and put his ear on the rock. He told them, "I can hear water running under this rock. If we are to be saved, we must not give up. Break the rock!"

There is water under this rock!

Though the men were tired, they did not give up. They struck the rock again and again with the hammer. They knew that they had to save everyone. Finally, the rock broke and in no time the hole was filled with water.

All the men and oxen drank water and bathed as well. Then, they broke the extra wooden yokes and axles kept in their carts for firewood. They lit a fire and cooked food. Everyone enjoyed a hearty meal before lying down to rest.

In the morning, the Merchant placed a flag near the spring so that other travellers could find the water easily. They resumed their journey at night and reached the

Let this spring help others also.

town the next morning. They sold their goods and earned huge profits.

Then they returned to their village happily.

**Moral:** One can overcome all odds with strong will and determination.

# The Merchant Of Seri

Once upon a time, there lived two merchants in the town of Seri. They both travelled from one town to the other, selling brass and tin utensils. One of the merchants was very greedy. He wanted to have everything for free, and if he bought

anything, he paid as little as he could. The other merchant was kind-hearted and honest, though he was not very rich.

One day, the merchants went to the same town. They divided the streets between themselves so that they would not interfere in each other's business, and could make profits. They also decided that once one was done with a street, the other could enter it. This way, both of them would get a chance to cover the town. So, they took their respective streets and started calling out, "Tinware utensils for sale! Brass utensils for sale!"

There lived a girl with her grandmother in one of the houses. Their family had

been rich once, but now they were poor. The only expensive thing they had was a golden plate. The grandmother did not know its worth and it lay among other unused utensils.

The greedy merchant passed this house, calling out, "Buy tin vessels! Buy brass utensils!"

The girl had not bought anything new for a long time and she felt tempted. She went to her grandmother and said, "Grandmother, please buy something for me."

The grandmother replied, "Child, we are very poor to buy anything. I don't even have anything to give in exchange for something new." The girl said, "We have

We will give the old plate to him.

an old plate, Grandmother. Let us see what the merchant will offer us in exchange for it. We don't even use it."

The grandmother finally agreed after seeing how excited the girl was. She called the merchant and showed him the plate. "Sir, will you take this plate and give us something new in return?" she asked.

The man took the plate and scratched it with a needle. He realised that it was made of gold. He became greedy and wanted the plate for free. He said, "It is not worth even half a penny!" He pretended not to be interested in the deal and walked away. He planned that he would come back after a while and take it from them for free.

Soon, the other merchant passed the house. The girl again asked her grandmother to see what this merchant would give for the plate.

"Grandmother, that merchant was bad-tempered, but this merchant looks like a gentleman. Please ask him!" she begged. The grandmother agreed and showed the plate to the merchant. As soon as he held the plate, the kind merchant realised that it was made of gold. He said, "This is a golden plate. I am not rich enough to buy it. You should sell it in the city where you will get a lot of money for it."

But the girl insisted, so the honest merchant said, "You can take whatever

you want in exchange for this plate."

The girl took some utensils of her choice, but the merchant felt guilty. He gave them all the money he had and all his goods, too. He told the grandmother that he needed a small amount of money for his return journey and she happily gave him the amount. The honest merchant took the money and the golden plate, and left.

A little later, the greedy merchant went back to the house and said to the girl, "Bring that plate and I will give you something for it!"

The grandmother replied, "You said the plate was worthless, but we just sold it to another merchant for a huge amount."

The merchant realised that he lost the

golden plate due to his greed. He went away, sadly. Meanwhile, the honest merchant went to the city and sold the plate. He received so much money for it that he was able to live comfortably for many years.

**Moral:** A bird in hand is worth two in the bush.

# The Hawks And Their Friends

Once, there lived a happy family of Hawks near a lake in a forest. Along the shore of the lake, there also lived a Lion, a Kingfisher and a Turtle.

One day, the Mother Hawk asked the Father Hawk, "My dear, how many

Befriend the Lion, Kingfisher and the Turtle.

friends do you have here?"

The Father Hawk replied, "I do have many friends, but none of them live in this part of the forest."

The Mother Hawk said, "You must make some friends nearby who can help us in times of need. The Kingfisher, the Lion and the Turtle could prove to be good friends."

So, the Father Hawk met all of them personally and made friends with them. They all were also very happy to have the Hawk family as their friend.

One day, some Hunters came to the forest. They hunted from morning till night in the forest and by the lake, but found nothing. Since they were very tired, they

made beds of leaves and lay down under the tree on which the Hawk family had their nest. However, the mosquitoes did not let them sleep. Finally, they got up and built a fire to drive away the mosquitoes with the smoke. This awoke the Hawks and the Baby Hawks began to cry.

"What is that sound?" asked an excited

Hunter. "It is the cry of birds from the nest up there. They will make for a very tasty breakfast!" said another Hunter.

They decided to climb up the tree to catch the Baby Hawks.

The frightened Mother Hawk said to her husband, "These men are planning to eat our young ones. We must ask our friends to

save us. Go and ask the Kingfisher for help."

The Father Hawk flew to the Kingfisher's nest and woke him up. The Kingfisher asked, "Why have you come here so late at night? Is everything all right?"

When the Father Hawk told him his problem, the Kingfisher said, "Don't worry, I will help you. Let us go to your nest."

When he reached the nest and saw the fire, the Kingfisher got an idea. He began to beat his wings rapidly and sprinkled water on the fire to put it out. As soon as the Hunters made another fire, the Kingfisher put it out again. This went on till midnight. The Mother Hawk said to her husband, "You must ask the Turtle to come and help

us while the Kingfisher gets some rest. I think he is very tired." The Father Hawk went and woke up the Turtle.

"What happened, friend?" asked the Turtle. The Father Hawk quickly told him everything.

"Of course, I will help you!" said the Turtle and at once went with the Hawk.

As the Turtle reached near the fire, he dived into the lake. Then he collected some mud from the bottom of the lake and doused the fire with it. When the Hunters saw the Turtle, they shouted in excitement, "Oh! Let us kill this Turtle. It will make for an even tastier breakfast. But, we have to be careful, so that he does not bite us. Let us

Enough! They will not build a fire now!

throw a net over him and trap him."

As the Hunters did not have a net, they took some vines and tore their clothes to make a net. When they tried to trap the Turtle, he suddenly dived and disappeared into the water. The hunters jumped into the lake. Alas! They not only missed him, but also became wet.

Once again, they decided to build a fire and eat the young Hawks instead.

The Mother Hawk said, "I am afraid sooner or later these men will get our young ones. Go and ask our friend, the Lion, to help us."

The Father Hawk flew to the Lion for help. At once, the Lion came with a roar. When

Friend, we are in great trouble.

they heard the Lion's roar, the frightened Hunters ran away. The Hawks were overjoyed and thanked all their friends. The Kingfisher and the Turtle also felt relieved that the Hawk family was safe, at last.

**Moral:** Friends in need are friends indeed.

# The Elephant And The Dog

Once upon a time, there lived an Elephant who was very dear to the King.

The Elephant was kept in the premises of the royal palace in a big, clean shed. He was fed well and bathed every day. His head was rubbed with perfumed oils,

while sandalwood paste and vermilion were smeared on his forehead daily.

A Dog lived near the Elephant's shed. He was very weak and thin, as he rarely got anything to eat. Naturally, the sweet smell of food being fed to the royal Elephant always made him hungry.

One day, sniffing the irresistible aroma

of the food, the Dog sneaked into the Elephant's shed. He ate the food that fell from the Elephant's mouth. He relished the food so much that he started sneaking in and eating it every day.

At first, the huge Elephant did not notice the small Dog enjoying his delicious food. Gradually, as the Dog became fatter and

Hey, wait! Who are you?

stronger, the Elephant started noticing him.

The Elephant started enjoying the company of the Dog and let him share his food. Both of them spent a lot of time together and soon they became very good friends. They ate, slept and played together. The Elephant would hold the Dog in his trunk and swing him back and forth. As their friendship grew, they did not want to be separated from one another.

One day, a man saw the Dog and asked the Mahout, "I want to buy this smart Dog. What price should I pay for him?"

Though the Mahout did not own the Dog, he sold him for a large sum of money. The

man took the Dog home. The Elephant became very sad to lose his friend. He missed him a lot and stopped eating, drinking and even bathing. The Mahout reported this to the King, but he did not say anything about the Dog.

The King had a wise Minister, who understood animal behaviour very well. He asked him to go to the Elephant's shed and find out the reason for his bad condition.

The Minister went to the shed and examined the Elephant carefully. He said to the Mahout, "There is nothing wrong with this Elephant, then why is he so sad? I think this Elephant is grief-stricken, maybe due to the loss of a dear friend. Do you

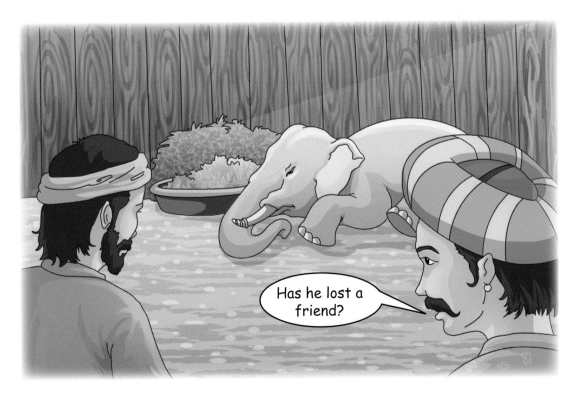

Has he lost a friend?

know whether he had any close friends?"

The Mahout said, "There was a Dog who used to eat, sleep and play with the Elephant. He was taken away by a stranger three days ago."

The Minister asked, "Where is the Dog?"

"I don't know, Sir," the Mahout replied.

The Minister returned to the King and

informed him, "Your Majesty, I think the Royal Elephant is not sick but is very lonely without his dear friend, the Dog."

The King said, "You are right, friendship is one of the most wonderful things in life. Do you know where that Dog is?"

The Minister replied, "The Mahout says that a stranger took him away, but he

knows nothing of his whereabouts."

"How can we bring back my Elephant's friend and make him happy again?" the King asked. The Minister suggested, "Your Majesty, make a declaration that the person who has the Dog will be punished."

On hearing the King's proclamation, the

man hurriedly turned the Dog loose.

Once free, the Dog ran back as fast as he could to reach the Elephant's shed. The Elephant was so delighted to see the Dog that he picked his friend with his trunk and made him sit on his head. The Dog wagged his tail happily while the Elephant's eyes sparkled with joy.

The King was pleased to see the Elephant happy once again. He rewarded the Minister for his wisdom. The Elephant and the Dog lived happily ever after.

**Moral:** True friends should never be separated.

# The Value Of Goodness

Once upon a time, there lived a wise Priest in the kingdom of King Brahmadatta of Benares (now known as Varanasi). He came from a noble family. He was intelligent and well-informed. He never shied away from sharing his wealth of knowledge.

The Priest led a simple and virtuous life. Impressed by his way of living, King Brahmadatta proclaimed, "This Priest is truly a good man!"

The Priest was curious to learn more about the value placed on goodness. He thought, 'The King honours and respects me. But is it because of my nationality, my noble birth or family wealth? Or is it due to my great learning and vast knowledge? Is it because of my goodness? I must find out the answer to this question.'

So, he decided to carry out an experiment to understand which virtue was most significant for human beings. He hatched a plan to steal from the King's treasury!

The next day, when he was leaving the palace, the Priest went to the coin-maker who was making gold coins for the treasury. The Priest picked up a coin and left quietly. Because the coin-maker admired the Priest, he said nothing.

The next day, the make-believe thief took two gold coins. Again, the coin-maker did not protest. Then on the third day, the Priest grabbed a handful of gold coins. This time, the coin-maker did not care about the Priest's reputation.

He cried out, "This is the third time you are taking the gold coins. That means you are robbing the King!"

Then, grabbing hold of the Priest, he

Are you really a good man?

screamed, "Help! Help! I have caught the thief who robs the King."

In no time, a crowd surrounded the Priest and yelled, "Priest! You pretended to be better than us. What a fine example of goodness is this!"

They tied his hands behind his back and decided to take him to the King.

On their way, they met some snake charmers, who were entertaining spectators in the palace premises. They held some snakes by their tail and neck, and coiled them around their necks.

The Priest said to them, "Please be careful. Don't grab the snakes by their tail or neck. Don't coil them around your necks.

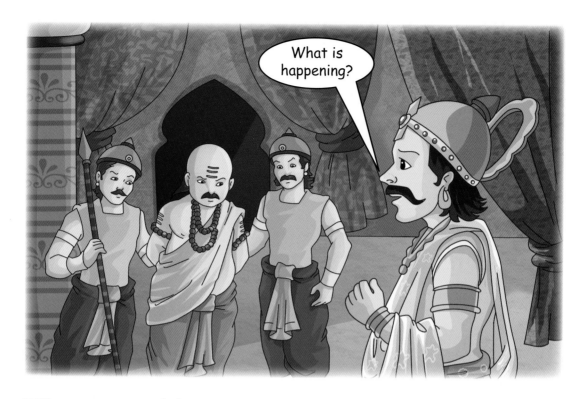

They may bite you!" The snake charmers ridiculed him and said, "You ignorant Priest, what do you know about these snakes? They are well-mannered and good, unlike you. You are a thief who has robbed the King! Because of your evil and criminal behaviour, you are being taken away to be punished."

The King was shocked to see the Priest with his hands tied behind his back!

The guards replied, "Your Highness, he was caught stealing gold coins from the treasury."

The King said, "Then, punish him!"

The Priest said, "Sir, I am not a thief."

"Then why did you take the gold coins

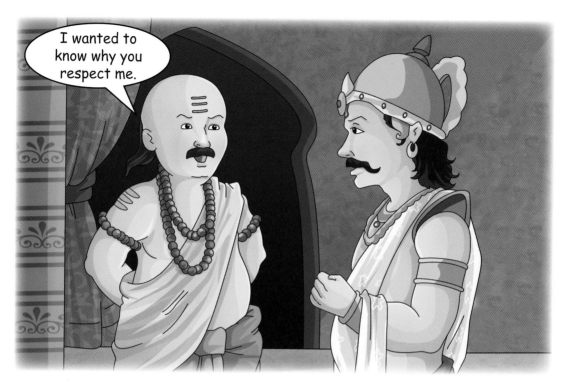

from the coin-maker?" asked the King.

The Priest explained, "Sir, this was only an experiment to find out which is the most desirable quality in a person. Are people respected because of their family background and wealth, or for their education and knowledge, or is it because of their goodness? I was able to get away easily when I took one or two gold coins. But when I grabbed a handful of coins, I was no longer 'good'.

"Even a poisonous snake that does not bite is called 'good' and is trusted. I found that there is no quality higher or more desirable than goodness. If there is no goodness, all nobility, education and knowledge mean

There is no quality higher than goodness.

nothing. On the other hand, a poisonous snake is also loved if it is good."

King Brahmadatta understood the Priest's words and pardoned him. Later, the Priest left the King's service forever, and went to the mountains to meditate.

**Moral:** Being good is the best quality.

# A Friend Named Jinx

Once upon a time, there was a very Rich Man, who was known for his wisdom. He had a good friend named Jinx. They had been the best of friends ever since they were children. They had gone to the same school, and had always been there for each other.

Unfortunately, Jinx had to go through hard times. He could not find a job and earn a living. One day, he went to meet his friend. His prosperous and successful friend was ready to help Jinx. He happily hired him to look after his huge mansion and business.

After Jinx started working in the Rich

Man's mansion, his strange name soon became a household word. People of the Rich Man's household used to say,

"Wait a minute, Jinx."

"Hurry up, Jinx."

"Do this, Jinx."

"Do that, Jinx."

One day, the neighbours said to the Rich

Man, "All of us are concerned that some misfortune may befall you soon. Your manager has a very unlucky name. You must send him away. His name fills your house and that is a bad omen. Usually people use the word 'jinx' only when they want to bring about bad luck or disaster. Even the good spirits and fairies will be frightened away, by hearing the word constantly. This man is miserable. What benefit can you possibly get by keeping Jinx around?"

The Rich Man replied, "Jinx is my best friend! We have cared and supported each other ever since we were children. I value my lifelong, trustworthy friend much more

than the meaning of his name. A name is only a means of identification. The wise people don't give any second thought to a name. Only fools are superstitious about words and names. Names don't bring good luck or bad luck. I refuse to shun him and fail him in his hour of need." Saying so, he told them to get rid of such illogical ideas.

A few days later, the Rich Man went on a business trip for a week, leaving his friend Jinx in charge of the mansion. It so happened that a gang of robbers heard about his journey. They decided that it would be the perfect time to rob the house. So, they armed themselves and surrounded the Rich Man's mansion at night.

Meanwhile, the vigilant Jinx suspected that something was wrong. He stayed up all night to guard his friend's possessions. When he saw the robbers surrounding the house, he woke up everybody. He asked the servants to blow trumpets, beat drums and make as much noise as possible. On hearing the noise, the robbers were startled. They realised that someone had seen them. So, they left their weapons and ran away as fast as they could.

The next morning, the neighbours were surprised to see the discarded weapons outside the Rich Man's mansion. They said to each other, "We were wrong about the manager. Jinx has turned out to be a

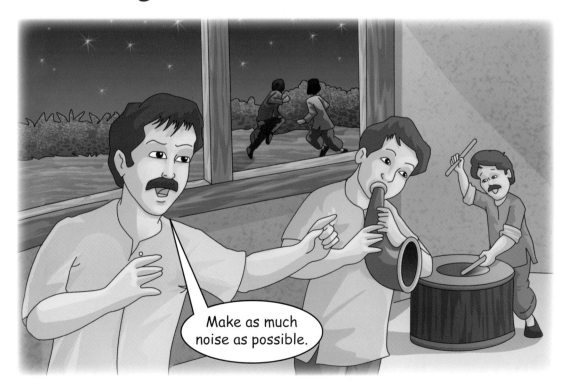

real hero. If he was not here, all the wealth in the mansion would certainly have been taken away. Rather than bringing bad luck, such a loyal friend has proved to be a blessing to the Rich Man."

When the Rich Man returned, he came to know about of what had happened in his absence. He was happy to hear that now his neighbours too believed in his friend, and he was right in having so much faith in Jinx. He hugged Jinx warmly and said, "Had it not been you, my friend, I would have been penniless today. I don't know how I can ever repay you for what you have done."

Jinx replied with tears in his eyes, "It was you who showed kindness when I needed

your help. In spite of what others said, you had faith in our friendship. Please do not embarrass me by your modesty. I only did my duty. Let us pledge to remain true friends for life."

**Moral:** A true friend is the greatest of all blessings.

# MEANINGS OF DIFFICULT WORDS

## Finding A New Spring

Axle
: a metal or wooden bar passing through the centre of a wheel or group of wheels

Halt
: bring or come to an abrupt stop

Merchant
: someone whose job is buying and selling goods, usually in large quantities

Resume
: to start something again after stopping temporarily

Yoke
: a wooden bar used for connecting animals that are pulling a vehicle or cart

## The Merchant Of Seri

Exchange
: the act of giving one thing and receiving another in return

Guilty
: ashamed of wrongdoing

| | |
|---|---|
| **Interfere** | : to deliberately get involved in other's affairs |
| **Pretend** | : to behave as if something is true when you know that it is not |
| **Utensil** | : something that you use for cooking or eating with |

## The Hawks And Their Friends

| | |
|---|---|
| **Douse** | : to put out a fire by pouring water; extinguish |
| **Shore** | : the land that is on the edge of a lake, river, or sea |
| **Vine** | : any type of plant that climbs or grows along the ground and has twisting stems |
| **Dive** | : to move downwards through water |

## The Elephant And The Dog

| | |
|---|---|
| **Mahout** | : a person who works with, rides, and tends an elephant |

| Grief-Stricken | : extremely sad |
| Irresistible | : too attractive and tempting to be resisted |
| Proclamation | : an official announcement |
| Relish | : to like or enjoy something |
| Smear | : spread something over a surface |
| Vermilion | : a bright red colour |
| Sniff | : to smell something by taking air in through your nose |
| Sneak | : to go somewhere quietly and secretly so that no one can see you or hear you |

## The Value Of Goodness

| Coil | : wind or twist into a continuous circular or spiral shape |
| Curious | : eager to learn more |
| Protest | : a strong complaint expressing disagreement, disapproval, or opposition |

| | |
|---|---|
| **Treasury** | : a place in which treasure is stored |
| **Experiment** | : a test done in order to learn something or to discover if something works or is true |
| **Grab** | : to take hold of something in a rough or rude way |
| **Make-believe** | : the activity of pretending that something is real |

## A Friend Named Jinx

| | |
|---|---|
| **Jinx** | : a person or a thing that is thought to bring bad luck |
| **Mansion** | : a large house |
| **Prosperous** | : rich and successful |
| **Shun** | : to deliberately avoid or ignore someone or something |
| **Vigilant** | : always being careful to notice things, especially possible danger |
| **Omen** | : a sign that shows whether good or bad things will happen in the future |